Gold Stars®

Maths

AGES
9-11
Key Stage 2

PaRRagon

Bath • New York • Cologne • Melbourne • Delhi
Hong Kong • Shenzhen • Singapore • Amsterdam

This edition published by Parragon Books Ltd in 2015

Parragon Books Ltd
Chartist House
15–17 Trim Street
Bath BA1 1HA, UK
www.parragon.com

Written by Paul Broadbent
Educational consultant: Martin Malcolm
Illustrated by Rob Davis/www.the-art-agency.co.uk
and Tom Connell/www.the-art-agency.co.uk

ISBN 978-1-4723-6039-7

Printed in China

Parents' notes

The Gold Stars Key Stage 2 series

The Gold Stars Key Stage 2 series has been created to help your child revise and practise key skills and information learned in school. Each book is a complete companion to the Key Stage 2 curriculum and has been written by an expert team of teachers. The books will help to prepare your child for SATs in Year 6 and other tests that they take at school.

The books also support Scottish National Guidelines 5-14.

How to use this workbook

- Talk through the introductions to each topic and review the examples together.

- Encourage your child to tackle the fill-in activities independently.

- Keep work times short. Skip a page if it seems too difficult and return to it later.

- It doesn't matter if your child does some of the pages out of order.

- Your child may need some extra scrap paper for working out on some of the pages.

- Check the answers on pages 60-63. Encourage effort and reward achievement with praise.

- If your child finds any of the pages too difficult, don't worry. Children learn at different rates.

Contents

Decimals

Learning objective: to read whole numbers and decimals

A decimal point separates whole numbers from decimal fractions - the parts of numbers that are less than 1.

> Decimals are often used to show the price of things.

Numbers use ten digits.

0   1   2   3   4   5   6   7   8   9

Look at this number.

37.84

3 tens   7 units   8 tenths   4 hundredths
(30)   (7) $\frac{8}{10}$ $\frac{4}{100}$

This is read as thirty-seven point eight four.

A Write the decimal number each arrow points to.

1. _____   2. _____   3. _____   4. _____

0   0.5   1

5. _____   6. _____   7. _____   8. _____   9. _____

8   8.5   9

10. _____   11. _____   12. _____   13. _____   14. _____

16   16.5   17

DEFINITION

decimal point: A point that separates whole numbers from decimal fractions.

B

This table shows the weight in kilograms of some of the turtles that swim in our seas. Write the list in order of weight, starting with the heaviest.

Turtle	Weight (kilograms)	Turtle	Weight (kilograms)
Flatback turtle	78.15		
Green sea turtle	355.3		
Hawksbill turtle	62.65		
Kemp's Ridley turtle	60.45		
Leatherback turtle	462.9		
Loggerhead turtle	257.8		

C

Rearrange this set of digits to make 6 different decimal numbers between 1 and 10. Use each digit only once in each decimal number.

1.

__.__ __ __.__ __ __.__ __ __.__ __ __.__ __ __.__ __

2. Write the decimal numbers you have made in order, starting with the smallest.

__.__ __ __.__ __ __.__ __ __.__ __ __.__ __ __.__ __

smallest →

7

Place value

Learning objective: to use place value to multiply and divide decimals by 10

The position of a digit in a number shows what the number is worth. This is what we mean by place value.

Making a number 10 times bigger or smaller is easy if you follow these rules.

To multiply any number by 10:
Move the digits one place to the left.

x10

To divide any number by 10:
Move the digits one place to the right.

÷10

A Answer these.

1. 1.35 x 10 = _____

2. 9.67 x 10 = _____

3. 68.5 ÷ 10 = _____

4. 334.6 ÷ 10 = _____

B Read and answer these.

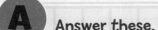

1.
A bucket holds
3.5 litres of water.
How much water
would there be in 10
buckets?

_____

2.
A car travels a total
of 9.85km each day.
How far does the car
travel after 10 days?

_____

3.
A 250kg sack of
grain is divided into
10 packs. How much
does each pack of
grain weigh?

_____

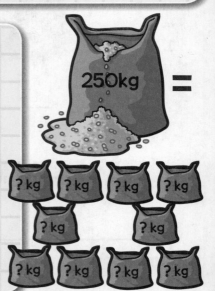

This is a super-square:

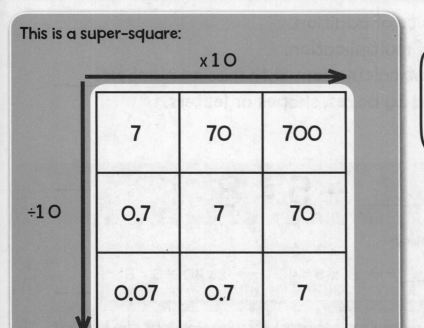

×10

7	70	700
0.7	7	70
0.07	0.7	7

÷10

Putting a zero on the end of a decimal number does not change the number. 3.8 is the same as 3.80!

c

Complete these super-squares.

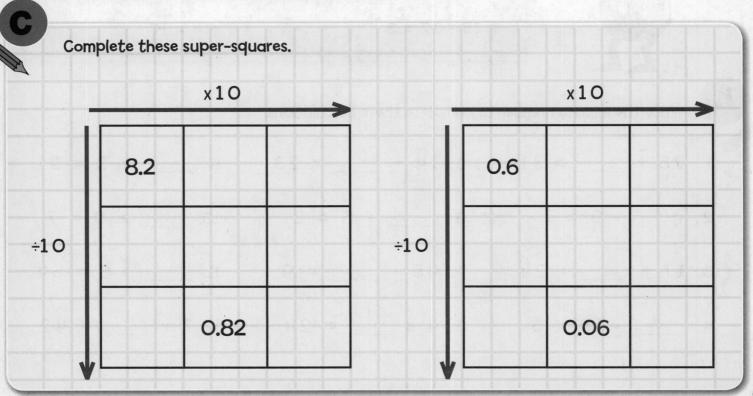

×10

8.2		
	0.82	

÷10

×10

0.6		
	0.06	

÷10

9

Mental calculation

Subtraction is the inverse or opposite of addition.
Division is the inverse or opposite of multiplication.
Use these facts to help you work out calculations with missing numbers.
Missing numbers can be represented by boxes, shapes or letters.

Knowing your multiplication tables and addition bonds is important.

_____ ÷ 5 = 8

Use multiplication:

8 x 5 = _____ → 8 x 5 = 40 → So 40 ÷ 5 = 8

When part of a problem is in brackets, you work out the bracket part first.

15 – (8 + 4) = _____   (15 – 8) + 4 = _____

15 – 12 = 3   7 + 4 = 11

A

Write the missing number to complete these calculations.

1. 25 + _____ = 31

2. _____ – 9 = 7

3. 17 + _____ = 24

4. _____ – 13 = 5

5. 14 + _____ = 23

6. _____ ÷ 6 = 2

7. 45 ÷ _____ = 9

8. 4 x _____ = 24

9. _____ x 3 = 21

10. _____ ÷ 9 = 7

11. _____ x 6 = 54

12. 7 x _____ = 42

DEFINITION

inverse: The opposite of something. For example forward is the inverse of backwards and, in maths, adding is the inverse of taking away.

B Write the answer for each of these. Remember to work out the brackets first.

1. (19 - 3) + 4 = _____

2. 14 - (7 + 2) = _____

3. (13 - 5) x 2 = _____

4. 16 - (8 - 3) = _____

5. 3 x (9 - 5) = _____

6. (4 + 6) ÷ 2 = _____

7. (8 + 2) - (3 + 5) = _____

8. (9 x 3) + (4 x 5) = _____

C Draw brackets to make each answer 12.

1. 19 - 12 - 5

2. 16 - 10 - 6

3. 22 - 5 + 5

4. 6 + 13 - 7

5. 24 - 6 - 6

6. 20 - 10 - 2

Try using opposite calculations to find the number.

D What's my number?
Work out the mystery number for each of these.

1. When I divide my number by 6 the answer is 8. _____

2. When I multiply my number by 6 the answer is 42. _____

3. When I double my number and then add 3 the answer is 19. _____

4. When I divide my number by 3 and then add 5 the answer is 12. _____

5. When I multiply my number by 5 and then subtract 6 the answer is 39. _____

6. When I divide my number by 4 and then subtract 2 the answer is 3. _____

Make up your own mystery number puzzles like this.

Square numbers

Learning objective: to know the squares of numbers up to 10 x 10

When two identical whole numbers are multiplied together they make a square number.

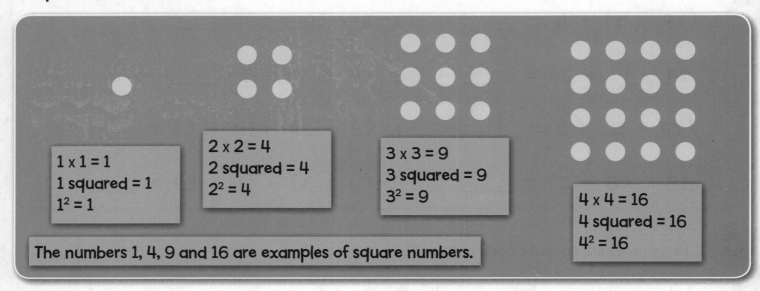

1 x 1 = 1
1 squared = 1
$1^2 = 1$

2 x 2 = 4
2 squared = 4
$2^2 = 4$

3 x 3 = 9
3 squared = 9
$3^2 = 9$

4 x 4 = 16
4 squared = 16
$4^2 = 16$

The numbers 1, 4, 9 and 16 are examples of square numbers.

A Write the missing numbers to complete this multiplication table.

	0	1	2	3	4	5	6	7	8	9	10
0	0	0		0	0			0	0		0
1			2			5	6	7		9	10
2	0		4	6	8				16	18	
3		3		9	12		18	21			
4	0							32			
5				15	20		30			45	
6											
7	0	7									
8		8		24		40		56		72	
9	0									81	
10		10			40				80		100

B

Colour the square for each of these in the multiplication table opposite.

1 x 1   2 x 2   3 x 3   4 x 4   5 x 5   6 x 6   7 x 7   8 x 8   9 x 9   10 x 10

What do you notice?

C

Circle the numbers in each set that are not square numbers.

1.   36   24   16   64   48

2.   25   81   9   15   12

3.   1   100   46   4   49

4.   18   49   9   81   77

5.   36   6   4   64   50

6.   49   9   39   100   92

Read across and down to multiply 2 numbers together. If you go across from 5 and down from 4 it meets at 20. So 5 x 4 = 20 and 4 x 5 = 20!

D

Answer these.

1. 4^2 = _____

2. 7^2 = _____

3. 6^2 = _____

4. 9^2 = _____

5. 1^2 = _____

6. 2^2 = _____

7. 10^2 = _____

8. 3^2 = _____

9. 8^2 = _____

10. 5^2 = _____

13

Multiples and factors

Learning objective: to identify pairs of factors and find common multiples

A multiple of a whole number is produced by multiplying that number by another whole number. Factors of a number can divide that number exactly.

Multiples of 3 →	3	6	9	12	15	18	21	24
Multiples of 4 →	4	8	12	16	20	24	28	32

12 is a multiple of both 3 and 4.
This means that 12 is a common multiple of 3 and 4.

10 has 4 factors because it can only be divided exactly by 4 numbers.

$$10 \div 1 = 10$$
$$10 \div 2 = 5$$
$$10 \div 5 = 2$$
$$10 \div 10 = 1$$

Factors of 10 in order: 1, 2, 5, 10
Factors of 10 in pairs: (1, 10) (2, 5)

Factors divide a number exactly.

Multiples mean more for me!

A Write all the pairs of factors for each of these numbers.

1. 8
   (__,__)   (__,__)

3. 24
   (__,__)   (__,__)

   (__,__)   (__,__)

2. 20
   (__,__)   (__,__)

   (__,__)

4. 28
   (__,__)   (__,__)

   (__,__)

DEFINITION

multiple: A multiple is a number made by multiplying together two other numbers.

DEFINITION

factor: A number that will divide exactly into other numbers. Example: 5 is a factor of 20.

B

Write the first 10 multiples for each of these numbers.

1. multiples of 4 → ____ ____ ____ ____ ____ ____ ____ ____ ____ ____
2. multiples of 3 → ____ ____ ____ ____ ____ ____ ____ ____ ____ ____
3. multiples of 6 → ____ ____ ____ ____ ____ ____ ____ ____ ____ ____
4. multiples of 5 → ____ ____ ____ ____ ____ ____ ____ ____ ____ ____
5. multiples of 10 → ____ ____ ____ ____ ____ ____ ____ ____ ____ ____
6. multiples of 8 → ____ ____ ____ ____ ____ ____ ____ ____ ____ ____

C

Look at your answers for Exercise B. Use the lists of multiples to help you find the common multiples for each of these pairs of numbers.

1. 3 and 5 → _____ _____
2. 4 and 3 → _____ _____
3. 4 and 5 → _____ _____

4. 6 and 8 → _____ _____
5. 10 and 6 → _____ _____
6. 6 and 4 → _____ _____ _____

D

Write these numbers in the correct part of the Venn diagram.

12   4̶   18
10̶   24̶   16̶
15   3   20
9   6   25
2   30   1

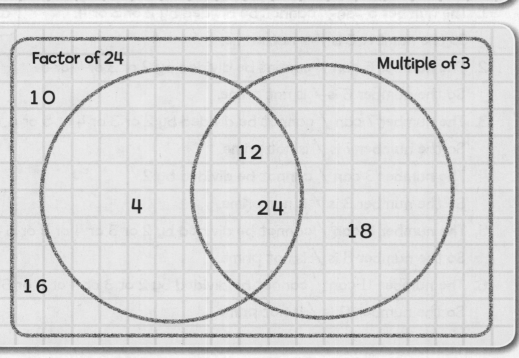

Factor of 24   Multiple of 3

10

12

4   24

18

16

15

Prime numbers

Learning objective: to recognize prime numbers

Prime numbers are special. You cannot divide them exactly by any other smaller number.

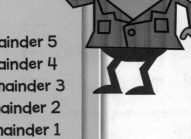

The only even prime number is 2. The other primes are all odd!

not prime

12 divides exactly by all these numbers . . .

12 ÷ 2 = 6
12 ÷ 3 = 4
12 ÷ 4 = 3
12 ÷ 6 = 2

prime

But 13 just won't divide exactly . . .

13 ÷ 2 = 6 remainder 1   13 ÷ 8 = 1 remainder 5
13 ÷ 3 = 4 remainder 1   13 ÷ 9 = 1 remainder 4
13 ÷ 4 = 3 remainder 1   13 ÷ 10 = 1 remainder 3
13 ÷ 5 = 2 remainder 3   13 ÷ 11 = 1 remainder 2
13 ÷ 6 = 2 remainder 1   13 ÷ 12 = 1 remainder 1
13 ÷ 7 = 1 remainder 6

A

Cross out the words to show the primes. The first two have been done for you.

Odd but true – maths experts say the number 1 doesn't count as a prime number!

1. The number 5 ~~can~~ / cannot be divided by 2 or 3 or 4.
   So the number 5 is / ~~is not~~ prime.

2. The number 6 can / ~~cannot~~ be divided by 2 or 3 ~~or 4 or 5~~.
   So the number 6 ~~is~~ / is not prime.

3. The number 7 can / cannot be divided by 2 or 3 or 4 or 5 or 6.
   So the number 7 is / is not prime.

4. The number 3 can / cannot be divided by 2.
   So the number 3 is / is not prime.

5. The number 8 can / cannot be divided by 2 or 3 or 4 or 5 or 6 or 7.
   So the number 8 is / is not prime.

6. The number 11 can / cannot be divided by 2 or 3 or 4 or 5 or 6 or 7 or 8 or 9 or 10.
   So the number 11 is / is not prime.

prime number: A whole number bigger than 1, that can't be exactly divided by any other whole number.

B

All the numbers in the green box can be divided by 2, 3 or 5 . . .

except for the prime numbers. Circle six more hidden primes.

15	48	25	(7)	18	44
62	11	20	12	36	
50	14	6	22	13	75
30	17	16	10	4	
90	26	24	27	33	19
100	35	55	60	8	
70	9	23	16	21	22
29	86	64	85	40	

C

This poem helps you remember all the prime numbers up to 20.

Fill in the missing rhymes.

They can't be divided, whatever you do

The smallest prime is number _____

Then come three and _____ and seven

The next prime is of course _____

_____ is next upon the scene

_____ follows and then _____ .

missing rhymes

seventeen   two

eleven   nineteen

five   thirteen

Written addition

Learning objective: to use efficient written methods to add whole numbers

When you add numbers like this, it helps to line up the columns. If a column adds up to 10 or more, carry the 10 over to the next column by writing a small number 1 beneath. Then add it with the numbers in that column.

The columns are: thousands, hundreds, tens and units.

What is 3492 added to 2631?

```
Th H T U
   3 4 9 2
 + 2 6 3 1
 ─────────
   6 1 2 3
     1 1
```

Look out for addition words in problems: add, total, sum, altogether, greater than...

A

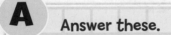

Answer these.

```
1.   6 7 2 8      2.   3 1 2 8      3.   1 5 6 1
   + 2 7 4 0         + 4 6 7 5         + 2 9 1 8
```

B

Read and answer these. Use a pen and paper to work out each calculation.

1. Add together 3945 and 5680. _____

2. What is 5929 and 3874 added together? _____

3. What is the sum of 2263 and 3815? _____

4. Total 5923 and 1946. _____

5. What is the total of 4328 and 2749? _____

6. What number is 4444 greater than 1991? _____

18

C

Look at these distances and work out the different totals.

A → 1652km   B → 3559km   C → 3081km   D → 2722 km   E → 1768km

1. A + E   →   _____ km

2. D + C   →   _____ km

3. B + D   →   _____ km

4. C + E   →   _____ km

5. E + D   →   _____ km

D

All the digits 1 and 3 are missing.

Write the digits 1 or 3 in the correct place to complete this addition.

```
    4 6 □ 8
  +
    9 □ 6 □
  ───────────
  □ □ 8 0 □
```

Use your knowledge of place value.

Write the numbers 1 and 3 on six small pieces of paper and try them in the different missing boxes to see which ones work.

19

Written subtraction

Learning objective: to use efficient written methods to subtract whole numbers

There are different ways of taking one number away from another. If you can't work it out in your head you can try a written method.

Example
What is 3674 subtract 1738?

Step 1

Think of 70 + 4 as 60 + 14

14 - 8 = 6

$$3\ 6\ ^6\!\!\not{7}\ ^1\!4$$
$$-1\ 7\ 3\ 8$$
$$\overline{\qquad\quad 6}$$

Step 2

60 - 30 = 30

$$3\ 6\ ^6\!\!\not{7}\ ^1\!4$$
$$-1\ 7\ 3\ 8$$
$$\overline{\qquad\ 3\ 6}$$

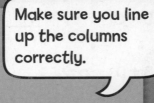
Make sure you line up the columns correctly.

Step 3

Think of 3000 + 600 as 2000 + 1600.

1600 - 700 = 900

$$^2\!\!\not{3}\ ^1\!6\ ^6\!\!\not{7}\ ^1\!4$$
$$-1\ 7\ 3\ 8$$
$$\overline{\quad\ 9\ 3\ 6}$$

Step 4

2000 - 1000 = 1000

$$^2\!\!\not{3}\ ^1\!6\ ^6\!\!\not{7}\ ^1\!4$$
$$-1\ 7\ 3\ 8$$
$$\overline{1\ 9\ 3\ 6}$$

A Write the answers.

1.
$$\begin{array}{r} 4\ 7\ 3\ 8 \\ -\ 1\ 5\ 9\ 2 \\ \hline \end{array}$$

2.
$$\begin{array}{r} 9\ 4\ 7\ 1 \\ -\ 3\ 8\ 0\ 3 \\ \hline \end{array}$$

3.
$$\begin{array}{r} 6\ 5\ 4\ 5 \\ -\ 2\ 1\ 7\ 5 \\ \hline \end{array}$$

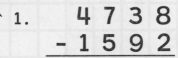

B

Write the missing digits in these subtractions.

1.
```
   3 8 4 ▢
 -  1 7 ▢ 2
 ──────────
   2 ▢ 8 5
```

2.
```
   7 ▢ 4 3
 -  2 4 8 ▢
 ──────────
   ▢ 4 5 7
```

3.
```
   4 1 1 5
 -  2 ▢ 3 ▢
 ──────────
   ▢ 1 7 9
```

C

This table shows the depths of the deepest oceans and seas in the world.

Look at the table and answer the questions.

Ocean/sea	Average depth (metres)
Pacific Ocean	4028 m
Indian Ocean	3963 m
Atlantic Ocean	3926 m
Caribbean Sea	2647 m
South China Sea	1652 m
Bering Sea	1547 m
Gulf of Mexico	1486 m
Mediterranean Sea	1429 m

1. How much deeper is the Caribbean Sea than the Gulf of Mexico? _____

2. By how many metres is the Pacific Ocean deeper than the Caribbean Sea? _____

3. What is the difference in depth between the Atlantic Ocean and the Caribbean Sea? _____

4. Which two seas have a difference in depth of 1100m? _____

5. Which sea is 1316m less in depth than the Indian Ocean? _____

6. Which two oceans or seas have the smallest difference in depth? _____

Written multiplication

Learning objective: to use written methods to multiply
TU (tens and units) x TU

When you need to multiply two numbers together, decide whether you are able to work out the answer in your head, or if you need to use a written method.

Look at these two written methods for 34 x 26.

Method 1

x	30	4
20	600	80
6	180	24

→ 680
→ + 204
884

Method 2

```
      3 4
    x 2 6
    2 0 4   (3 4 x 6)
    6 8 0   (3 4 x 2 0)
    8 8 4
```

It is always a good idea to estimate the answer first and then check your final answer with your estimate.

A Complete these multiplications.

1. 1 9 x 7 6 = _____

2. 8 4 x 3 7 = _____

3.
```
      1 9
    x 2 4
```

4.
```
      5 3
    x 6 2
```

22

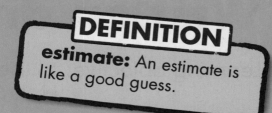
B   Read and answer these questions.

1. There are 24 hours in a day. How many hours are there in September? _____

2. A truck makes a 58km journey 16 times in a week. How far does the truck travel in total?

   _____

3. A packet of nuts weighs 28g and there are 25 packets in a box. How many grams of nuts are there in a full box? _____

4. There are 15 pencils in a pack and a school orders 49 packs. How many pencils will there be altogether? _____

C

How many of each item has been ordered?

This is an order form for equipment for a school.

Items	Amount in 1 pack	Number of packs	Total number of items
Pencils	28	76	
Chalk	15	33	
Sharpeners	26	19	
Erasers	48	14	
Pens	52	58	
Crayons	34	47	

D

Write the digits 3, 4, 5 and 6 on small pieces of paper.

Using all 4 digits, arrange the numbers to make different multiplications.

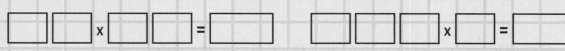

1. What is the largest answer you can make?
2. What is the smallest answer?
3. What answer is the nearest you can make to 1000?

Written division

Learning objective: to use written methods to divide
H (hundreds) TU ÷ U

Some dividing you can do in your head as it links with multiplying. 48 divided by 6 is 8, which is easy if you know that 6 x 8 is 48. When you divide bigger numbers, you need to use a written method.

Remember!
If a number cannot be divided exactly it leaves a remainder.

What is 749 divided by 4?

Work out how many groups of 4 are in 749 and what is left over:

Method 1

```
    187 r1
4 )7 4 9
  -4 0 0    (4 x 100)
   3 4 9
  -3 2 0    (4 x 80)
     2 9
    -2 8    (4 x 7)      749 ÷ 4 = 187 remainder 1
       1
```

Method 2

```
       187 r1
4 )7³4 ²9
```

700 ÷ 4 = 100
Carry 300 over to the tens.
340 ÷ 4 = 80
Carry 20 over to the units.
29 ÷ 4 = 7
The remainder is 1.

A Complete these divisions and write the answers with remainders.

1. 4 8 8 ÷ 3 → _____ r __
   3)4 8 8

3. 1 8 9 ÷ 4 → _____ r __
   4)1 8 9

2. 3 6 7 ÷ 5 → _____ r __
   5)3 6 7

4. 9 2 6 ÷ 4 → _____ r __
   4)9 2 6

Use paper for written workings out.

B Draw a line to match each remainder to a division.

271 ÷ 6

315 ÷ 8

454 ÷ 5

608 ÷ 3

Remainder
1
2
3
4
5
6
7
8
9

149 ÷ 6

259 ÷ 9

359 ÷ 10

458 ÷ 9

398 ÷ 7

C

Eggs are collected every day and put into boxes of 6. Write how many full boxes can be made each day and how many eggs are left over to complete this chart.

Day of the week	Eggs collected	Number of	
		Full boxes (6 eggs)	Eggs left over
Monday	627		
Tuesday	572		
Wednesday	700		
Thursday	644		
Friday	683		
Saturday	594		
Sunday	735		

Rounding numbers

Learning objective: to use rounding and approximation to estimate calculations

We round numbers to make them easier to work with. It is useful for estimating approximate, or rough, answers.

Decimal numbers can be rounded to the nearest whole number or tenth. Whole numbers can be rounded to the nearest 10, 100 or 1000. Round down if the digit is less than 5. Round up if the digit is 5 or more.

To round decimals to the nearest whole number, look at the **tenth** digit.

4.**4**7 round down to 4
12.**7**5 round up to 13

To round numbers to the nearest 10, look at the **units** digit.

2**4** round down to 20
8**5** round up to 90

To round large numbers to the nearest 100, look at the **tens** digit.

68**2**8 round down to 6800
304**5**9 round up to 30500

To round large numbers to the nearest 1000, look at the **hundreds** digit.

68**4**28 round down to 68000
304**6**59 round up to 305000

A This chart shows some cities with a population of less than 1 million. Round each population to the nearest 100.

Tip: focus on the last 3 digits in each number.

Town	Population	Nearest 100
Liverpool	469019	
Bradford	293717	
Sheffield	439866	
Derby	229407	
Birmingham	970892	
Nottingham	249584	
Bristol	420556	
Plymouth	243795	

DEFINITION

approximate answer:
An answer that is close to the right answer, but not exact.

B Round each number to the nearest 100, then do the sum.

1. 415 + 388 → _____   4. 378 + 836 → _____

2. 682 - 174 → _____   5. 2190 + 3675 → _____

3. 597 - 489 → _____   6. 9251 + 4359 → _____

C Round each of these to the nearest whole number of kilograms. Write the approximate total weights for each set.

1. 4.38 kg   2.97 kg   9.19 kg   Approx. total weight _____ kg
2. 9.49 kg   7.73 kg   3.64 kg   Approx. total weight _____ kg
3. 13.85 kg   12.55 kg   6.53 kg   Approx. total weight _____ kg
4. 19.09 kg   17.64 kg   8.47 kg   Approx. total weight _____ kg

D Calculators can display lots of decimal places. We often round off numbers to 2 decimal places.

| 0.76398 | → rounds down to | 0.76 |
| 3.42739 | → rounds up to | 3.43 |

Round these to 2 decimal places.

1. 0.9286 _____   2. 7.0835 _____   3. 12.945 _____
4. 7.5881 _____   5. 2.9116 _____   6. 30.0794 _____

Decimal calculations

Learning objective: to use written methods to add and subtract decimals

Some decimals you can add and subtract in your head, but other bigger numbers will need a written method.

Adding and subtracting decimals is just like adding and subtracting whole numbers. Just remember that the decimal point in the answer is in line with the decimal points above.

Example 1

What is 12.78 added to 37.41?

An approximate answer is 13 + 37 = 50

```
   12.78
 + 37.41
   50.19
   1  1
```

Example 2

What is 34.82 subtract 19.96?

An approximate answer is 35 – 20 = 15

```
  ²3 ¹³4 . ¹⁷8 ¹2
 - 1  9 . 9  6
   1  4 . 8  6
```

A Complete these additions.

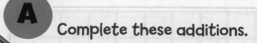

1. 45.37
  + 22.46

2. 31.85
  + 52.91

3. 73.02
  + 18.79

4. 64.89
  + 20.62

B Complete these subtractions.

1. 77.86
  - 34.84

2. 90.52
  - 43.29

3. 65.19
  - 27.43

4. 58.03
  - 16.25

It is always a good idea to estimate an approximate answer first, so you can check your answer against your estimate.

DEFINITION

difference: The difference between two numbers is the amount by which one number is greater than the other. The difference between 18 and 21 is 21 - 18 = 3.

C

Write the total measurements.

1. 13.88L + 12.75L _____

2. 47.39m + 16.52m _____

3. 35.04kg + 32.97kg _____

4. 59.87m + 21.36m _____

D

This chart shows the gymnasts' scores for four events. Using information from the chart answer the questions below.

Name	Horse Vault	Uneven Bars	Balance Beam	Floor Exercise
Eileen	18.10	19.16	18.96	19.36
Sandra	18.40	19.40	19.02	19.00
Nikki	19.16	18.89	18.66	18.96
Julie	19.19	19.26	19.13	19.20
Stacey	19.03	18.99	19.22	18.70

1. What is the difference between the Horse Vault scores of Sandra and Nikki? _____

2. What is the difference between the highest and lowest scores on the Uneven Bars?_____

3. Which two gymnasts have a difference of 0.4 in their Floor Exercise scores? _____

4. How many more points did Julie need on the Balance Beam to match the top score for this event?_____

5. The scores were each out of 20. How far from full marks was Nikki on the Balance Beam?_____

Simplifying fractions

Learning objective: to reduce a fraction to its simplest expression

With some fractions, it's hard to picture exactly what they mean.

The numerator (the number on the top) and the denominator (the number on the bottom) are both bigger than they need to be. Like this:

$$\frac{20}{25}$$

You can make fractions like this simpler and easier to understand if you can spot a number that divides both the numerator and denominator.

$$20 \div 5 = 4$$
$$25 \div 5 = 5$$

so → $\frac{20}{25}$ is the same as $\frac{4}{5}$

You must use the same number to divide the top and bottom of the fraction.

A   Simplify these fractions.

1. $6 \div 3 =$
   $21 \div 3 =$
   so → $\frac{6}{21}$ is the same as ___

2. $9 \div 3 =$
   $15 \div 3 =$
   so → $\frac{9}{15}$ is the same as ___

3. $4 \div 2 =$
   $6 \div 2 =$
   so → $\frac{4}{6}$ is the same as ___

4. $12 \div 6 =$
   $18 \div 6 =$
   so → $\frac{12}{18}$ is the same as ___

DEFINITION

simplify: To make something easier to understand.

Hint: all even numbers divide by 2. All numbers that end with 0 divide by 10. And all numbers that end with 0 or 5 divide by 5.

B

Find the right number to simplify each fraction. Choose from **2, 5** or **10**.

1. 15 ÷ ___ =
    40 ÷ ___ =   **so** ➤ $\frac{15}{40}$ is the same as ___

2. 14 ÷ ___ =
    16 ÷ ___ =   **so** ➤ $\frac{14}{16}$ is the same as ___

3. 8 ÷ ___ =
    12 ÷ ___ =   **so** ➤ $\frac{8}{12}$ is the same as ___

4. 20 ÷ ___ =
    30 ÷ ___ =   **so** ➤ $\frac{20}{30}$ is the same as ___

C

Match each circle to a diamond.

 $\frac{9}{18}$

$\frac{4}{5}$

$\frac{12}{15}$

$\frac{3}{4}$

$\frac{2}{3}$

$\frac{5}{6}$

$\frac{50}{60}$

$\frac{10}{15}$

$\frac{11}{33}$

$\frac{1}{2}$

$\frac{7}{28}$

$\frac{1}{3}$

$\frac{18}{24}$

$\frac{1}{4}$

Comparing fractions

Learning objective: to know how to compare and order a set of fractions

You may need to work out which fraction is bigger when you are comparing amounts.

For example, which would give you more of a cake: $\frac{2}{3}$ of it, or $\frac{3}{4}$ of the cake? This is tricky with different denominators.

Comparing fractions with the same denominator is easy:
For example, $\frac{4}{5}$ is bigger than $\frac{2}{5}$

$\frac{4}{5}$

$\frac{2}{5}$

To compare any fractions change them to equivalent fractions with a common denominator. This means they have the same denominator.

Example
Which is the larger fraction: $\frac{2}{3}$ or $\frac{3}{4}$? Find the equivalent fractions to $\frac{2}{3}$ and $\frac{3}{4}$ that have a common denominator.

$$\frac{2}{3} = \frac{4}{6} = \frac{6}{9} = \mathbf{\frac{8}{12}} \qquad \frac{3}{4} = \frac{6}{8} = \mathbf{\frac{9}{12}}$$

$\frac{9}{12}$ is larger than $\frac{8}{12}$

$\frac{3}{4}$ is larger than $\frac{2}{3}$

$$\frac{3}{4} > \frac{2}{3}$$

A Complete these to make a chain of equivalent fractions.

1. $\dfrac{1}{3} = \dfrac{\square}{6} = \dfrac{3}{\square} = \dfrac{\square}{12} = \dfrac{5}{\square} = \dfrac{\square}{\square}$

2. $\dfrac{1}{4} = \dfrac{2}{\square} = \dfrac{\square}{12} = \dfrac{4}{\square} = \dfrac{\square}{20} = \dfrac{\square}{\square}$

3. $\dfrac{1}{2} = \dfrac{\square}{4} = \dfrac{3}{\square} = \dfrac{\square}{8} = \dfrac{5}{\square} = \dfrac{\square}{\square}$

4. $\dfrac{2}{3} = \dfrac{4}{\square} = \dfrac{\square}{9} = \dfrac{8}{\square} = \dfrac{\square}{15} = \dfrac{\square}{\square}$

B Write < or > or = between each pair of fractions.
Use your completed equivalent fractions chains from Exercise A
to help you change them to equivalent fractions.

< means less than.
> means more than.

1. $\frac{2}{3}$ $\frac{1}{2}$ 2. $\frac{1}{4}$ $\frac{1}{3}$

3. $\frac{2}{3}$ $\frac{4}{5}$ 4. $\frac{4}{5}$ $\frac{1}{2}$

C Draw a line and join each of these fractions to its correct place on this number line.

0   0.5   1

| $\frac{1}{10}$ | $\frac{3}{4}$ | $\frac{9}{10}$ | $\frac{2}{5}$ | $\frac{1}{5}$ | $\frac{7}{10}$ | $\frac{6}{10}$ | $\frac{1}{2}$ | $\frac{3}{5}$ | $\frac{1}{4}$ | $\frac{3}{10}$ | $\frac{4}{5}$ |

D Put each group of fractions in order starting with the smallest.

1. $\frac{1}{4}$ $\frac{3}{8}$ $\frac{1}{2}$ $\frac{10}{16}$

2. $\frac{1}{6}$ $\frac{1}{3}$ $\frac{3}{4}$ $\frac{6}{12}$

Equivalents

Learning objective: to find equivalent percentages, decimals and fractions

When something is part of a whole, it can be displayed as a fraction, decimal or percentage.

Look at this grid.
25% of the grid is red.

$$\frac{5}{20} = \frac{25}{100} = 25\%$$

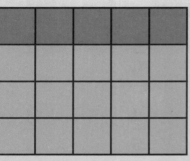

25% is the same as $\frac{1}{4}$.

Look at these methods for converting between fractions, percentages and decimals:

Per cent to decimal

Divide the percentage by 100

Example: 60% is the same as 0.6

Decimal to per cent

Multiply the decimal by 100

Example: 0.25 is the same as 25%

Per cent to fraction

Write the percentage as a fraction out of 100 and then simplify

Example: 40% is $\frac{40}{100}$, which is the same as $\frac{2}{5}$

Fraction to per cent

Write the fraction as a decimal and then multiply by 100

Example: $\frac{3}{4}$ is 0.75 which is the same as 75%

A Use the methods shown above to change these fractions and decimals to percentages.

Turn to page 6 for revision on decimals.

1. $\frac{3}{10}$ _____ 2. $\frac{1}{5}$ _____ 3. $\frac{7}{100}$ _____ 4. $\frac{11}{50}$ _____

5. 0.8 _____ 6. 0.1 _____ 7. 0.65 _____ 8. 0.12 _____

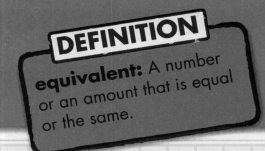
B   Write the missing digits to complete these.

1. $\frac{1}{2}$ = 0._____ = 50%

2. $\frac{1}{4}$ = 0.25 = _____%

3. $\frac{1}{20}$ = 0.05 = _____%

4. $\frac{2}{\boxed{}}$ = 0.4 = 40%

5. $\frac{17}{50}$ = 0._____ = 34%

6. $\frac{7}{10}$ = 0.7 = _____%

C   Write the fraction and percentage shown by the shaded part of each shape.

1.

2.

3.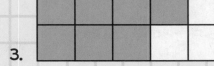

4.

5.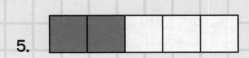

6.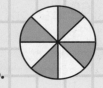

D   Write the percentages for each of these headlines.

1.   There was a one-in-a-hundred chance of finding the treasure.

     There was a _____% chance of finding the treasure.

2.   Eight out of ten children like maths more than any other subject.

     _____% of children like maths more than any other subject.

3.   Four in five people read our newspaper!

     _____% of people read our newspaper!

4. Our football team won sixteen of their last twenty matches.

     Our football team won _____% of their last twenty matches.

Percentages

Learning objective: to find percentages of whole number quantities

Percentages are simply fractions out of 100. 'Per cent' means 'out of 100' and the percentage sign is %.

We often need to work out percentages of amounts.
For example, what is 20% of 60 metres?
In examples like this, 'of' means multiply, so this is 20% x 60.
Look at these two methods to work this out.

Method 1

If you can multiply fractions, change the percentage to a fraction and work it out:

$$20\% = \frac{20^1}{100^5} = \frac{1}{5} \quad \text{and} \quad 60m = \frac{60}{1}$$

$$\frac{1}{5} \times \frac{60}{1} = \frac{60^{12}}{5^1} = 12m$$

Method 2

The quick method is to use 10% to work it out. 10% is 1/10, which is the same as dividing a number by 10:

10% of 60 is 6.

So, 20% of 60m is double that: 12m

A

Write these percentages as fractions in their lowest terms.

For example: $30\% = \frac{30}{100} = \frac{6}{20} = \frac{3}{10}$

1. 40% ☐ → ☐ → ☐

2. 80% ☐ → ☐ → ☐

3. 25% ☐ → ☐ → ☐

'Lowest terms' means using small numbers.

DEFINITION

percentage: This is a fraction out of 100, shown with a % sign.

B

These are the marks that Joseph scored in some maths tests. Change them all to percentages to work out which test he scored highest in and which was his lowest score.

Test	Score	Percentage
1	$\frac{7}{10}$	
2	$\frac{18}{20}$	
3	$\frac{4}{5}$	

Test	Score	Percentage
4	$\frac{21}{25}$	
5	$\frac{38}{50}$	

Highest score in test _____

Lowest score in test _____

C   Write these amounts.

1. 10% of 70cm = _____

2. 30% of 90km = _____

3. 20% of 20 litres = _____

4. 40% of 30kg = _____

5. 50% of 70ml = _____

6. 25% of 80m = _____

7. 10% of 600g = _____

8. 50% of 400mm = _____

You can revise percentages and fractions on page 34.

D

This chart shows different percentages of each length. Complete the chart by writing in the missing lengths.

	50%	25%	10%	40%	5%
60m	30m				3m
50m		12.5m			
300m				120m	
250m			25m		

37

Proportion

Learning objective: to solve simple problems involving proportions of quantities

Finding the proportion of an amount is the same as finding the fraction of the whole amount. A proportion can be written as a fraction.

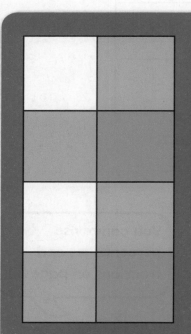

What proportion of the tiles are white?
When you look at the proportion of an amount, it is the same as finding the fraction of the whole amount.
There are 8 tiles altogether, 2 of them are white, so 2/8 of the tiles are white.
This means that the proportion of white tiles is 1 in every 4, or 1/4.

Two quantities are in direct proportion when they increase or decrease in the same ratio.
For example, if 3 apples weigh 300g, what is the weight of 15 apples?
This is 5 times the number of apples, so it is five times the weight: 300g x 5 = 1500g (or 1.5kg).

A Look at these tile patterns. What proportion of each of the patterns is blue?

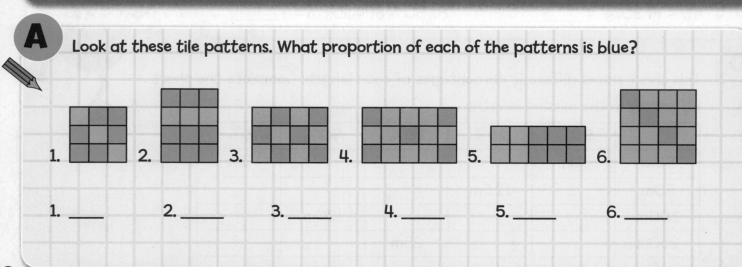

1. ____ 2. ____ 3. ____ 4. ____ 5. ____ 6. ____

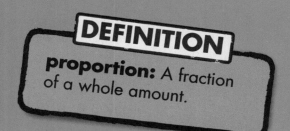

DEFINITION

proportion: A fraction of a whole amount.

B

Complete these tables showing the proportion of fruit in juice drinks.

The fruits are measured in fifths. The proportion of fruit stays the same in each table.

1.

Pineapples	Oranges	Total
1	4	5
2	8	
	20	
8		
10		

2.

Bananas	Peaches	Total
2	3	5
4	6	
	18	
16		
		50

C

In these recipes the amount of each ingredient is given as a proportion of the total weight.

Write the missing weights of each ingredient in these two recipes.

1. **600g Carrot and walnut cake**

1/4 butter   150g

1/3 flour   200g

1/6 grated carrots _____g

1/10 sugar _____g

1/12 beaten eggs _____g

1/15 walnuts _____g

2. **360g Chocolate chip cookies**

1/2 flour _____g

1/4 butter _____g

1/6 sugar _____g

1/12 chocolate chips _____g

D

What weight of ingredients are needed for a 1.2kg carrot and walnut cake?

butter _____g

flour _____g

grated carrots _____g

sugar _____g

beaten eggs _____g

walnuts _____g

2D shapes

Learning objective: to describe the properties of polygons

Polygons are straight-sided, closed shapes. Quadrilaterals are any shapes with 4 straight sides.

Learn the properties of these different polygons.

Number of sides		Name	Number of sides		Name
3		Triangle	6		Hexagon
4		Quadrilateral	7		Heptagon
5		Pentagon	8		Octagon

Learn the properties of these different quadrilaterals.

Square
- 4 equal sides
- 4 right angles

Rectangle
- 2 pairs of equal sides
- 4 right angles

Rhombus
- 4 equal sides
- opposite angles equal
- opposite sides parallel

Parallelogram
- opposite sides are equal and parallel
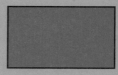

Kite
- 2 pairs of adjacent sides that are equal

Trapezium
- 1 pair of parallel sides

DEFINITION

adjacent: Being positioned next to something else.

DEFINITION

parallel: Two or more lines that are the same distance apart.

A

Count the sides and write the name for each shape.

1. _____

2. _____

3. _____

4. _____

5. _____

6. _____

2D means two-dimensional. Am I a 2D shape?

B

Name each of these quadrilaterals.

1. _____

2. _____

3. _____

4. _____

5. _____

6. _____

C

Complete these sentences by writing <u>always</u>, <u>sometimes</u> or <u>never</u>.

Look at the shapes on these two pages to help you.

1. A rectangle _____ has 4 right angles.

2. An octagon _____ has 7 sides.

3. The opposite sides of a parallelogram are _____ parallel.

4. The sides of a square are _____ equal.

5. A triangle _____ has a right angle.

6. The sides of a rhombus are _____ the same length.

Angles

Learning objective: to calculate angles in straight lines and triangles

The amount by which something turns is an angle.
Angles are measured in degrees (°). There are 360° in a circle.
These are some special angles to remember:

90° (right angle)

An acute angle is less than a right angle.

A device called a protractor can be used to measure angles.

180° (straight angle)

An obtuse angle is between 90° and 180°.

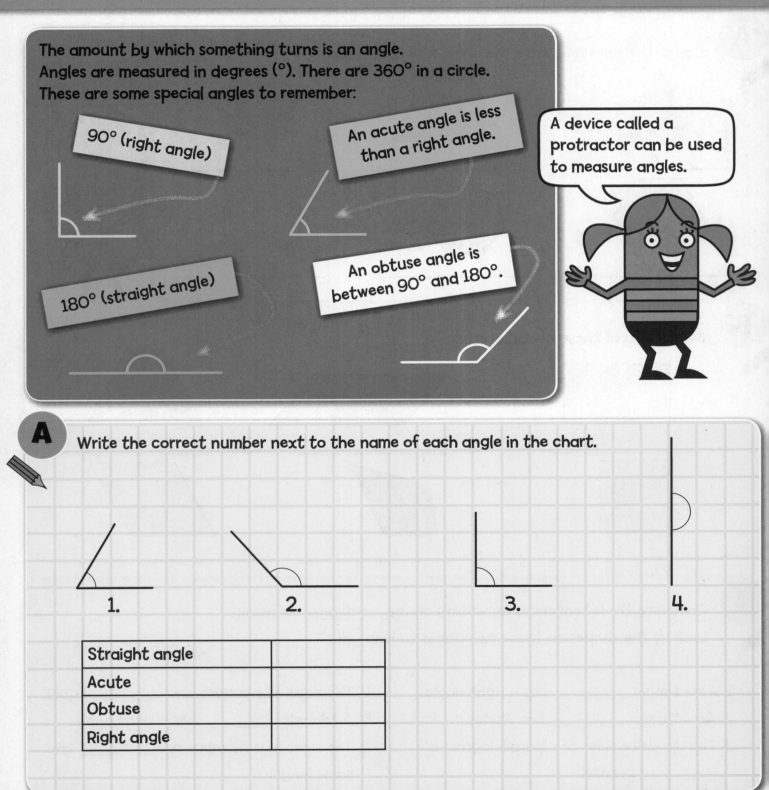

A Write the correct number next to the name of each angle in the chart.

1.   2.   3.   4.

Straight angle	
Acute	
Obtuse	
Right angle	

B Angles in a triangle always add up to 180°. Write the missing angle on these triangles.

1.  69° 68°

2. 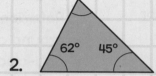 62° 45°

3. 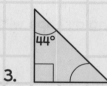 44°

C Angles in a straight line always add up to 180°. Write the missing angles below.

1.  104°

2. 66°

3. 120°

4. 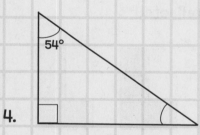 54°

5. 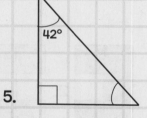 42°

6. 78°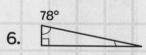

D Write the two missing angles on these.

Remember that a right angle always measures 90°.

1. 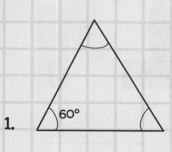 60°

2. 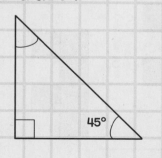 45°

Moving shapes

Learning objective: to draw shapes on grids after translation, reflection or rotation

A shape can be moved by translation, reflection or rotation.

Translation: sliding a shape without rotating or flipping over.

This shape has moved 4 squares across and 1 square down.

Reflection: this is sometimes called a 'flip'.

Rotation: a shape can be rotated around a point, clockwise or anti-clockwise.
Shape A is rotated clockwise around point X to become shape B.

Point X

A Write whether these shapes have been translated, rotated or reflected.

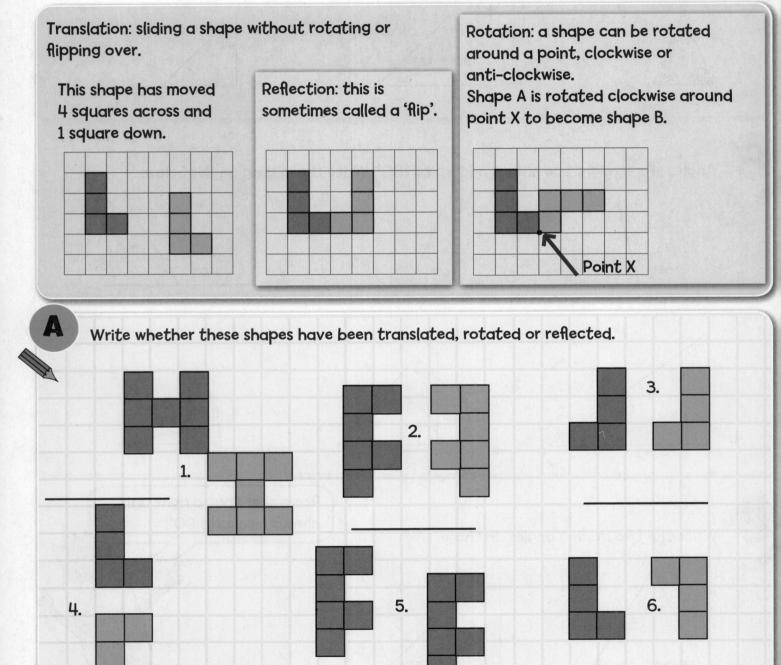

1.

2.

3.

4.

5.

6.

44

DEFINITION

clockwise: Moving in the same direction as the hands of a clock.

DEFINITION

anti-clockwise: Moving in the opposite direction to the hands of a clock.

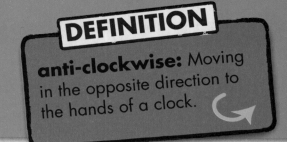

B

Repeat these shape tiles to design a larger pattern.

Decide whether to rotate, reflect or translate each tile.

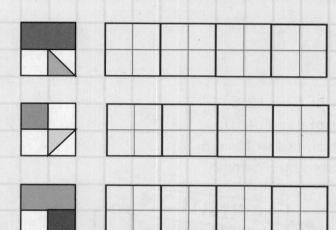

Can you make a symmetrical pattern?

C

Copy this tile and repeat it 10 times.

Use it to make a pattern of translated, rotated or reflected tiles.

Design your own tile and explore the patterns you can make.

Coordinates

Coordinates are used to show an exact position of a point on a grid.
Two numbers from the x and y axes show the position.

Look at the graph.

The number on the horizontal x axis is written first, then the vertical y axis. You can remember this because x comes before y in the alphabet!

The coordinates of A are (2, 5)
The coordinates of B are (4, 3)
Coordinates are always written in brackets separated by a comma.

DEFINITION

axis: The horizontal or vertical line on a graph. Plural is **axes**.

A

1. A, B and C are corners of a rectangle. What are the coordinates of the fourth corner?

2. P, Q and R are corners of a parallelogram. What are the coordinates of the fourth corner?

46

DEFINITION

vertices: The corners of 3D shapes, where edges meet. Singular is **vertex**.

B

Look at how each of these triangles has moved. Write the coordinates of the vertices of both triangles for each of them.

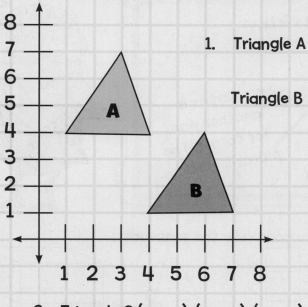

1. Triangle A   (1, 4), (3, 7), (4, 4)

     Triangle B   (__,__), (__,__), (__,__)

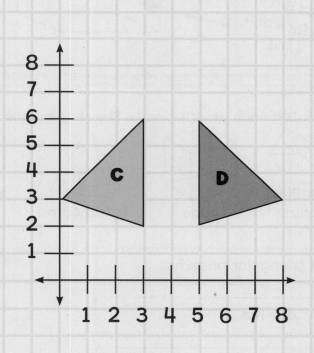

2. Triangle C (__,__), (__,__), (__,__)

     Triangle D (__,__), (__,__), (__,__)

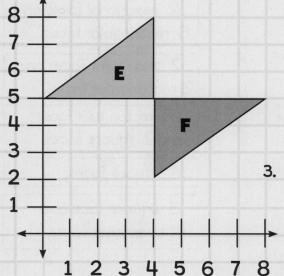

3. Triangle E (__,__), (__,__), (__,__)

     Triangle F (__,__), (__,__), (__,__)

3D shapes

Learning objective: to describe the properties of 3D shapes

A solid shape has three dimensions: height, length and width.

Solid or 3D shapes are made up of faces, edges and vertices (corners).

A cuboid has 6 faces, 12 edges and 8 vertices.

An edge is where two faces meet.

A face is a flat surface of a solid.

Vertex is another word for corner. The plural is vertices.

What shape is a cereal box?

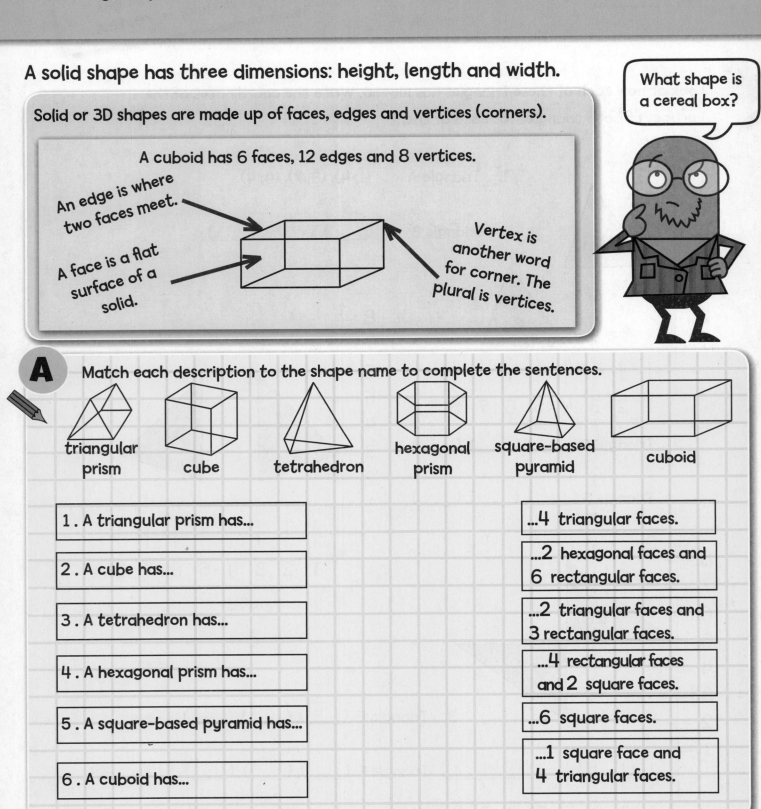

A Match each description to the shape name to complete the sentences.

triangular prism   cube   tetrahedron   hexagonal prism   square-based pyramid   cuboid

1. A triangular prism has...

2. A cube has...

3. A tetrahedron has...

4. A hexagonal prism has...

5. A square-based pyramid has...

6. A cuboid has...

...4 triangular faces.

...2 hexagonal faces and 6 rectangular faces.

...2 triangular faces and 3 rectangular faces.

...4 rectangular faces and 2 square faces.

...6 square faces.

....1 square face and 4 triangular faces.

Prisms

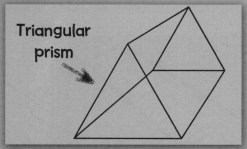

Triangular prism

Prisms have rectangular faces, with the shape of the end face giving each prism its name.

Cuboids and cubes are special types of prism.

Pyramids

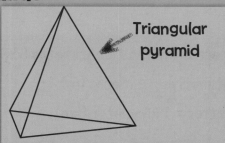

Triangular pyramid

The shape of the base gives each pyramid its name. The triangular faces of a pyramid all meet at a point.

Another name for a triangular pyramid is a tetrahedron.

B Sort these shapes into prisms and pyramids. Complete the table below.

A

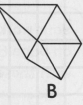

B

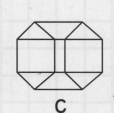

C

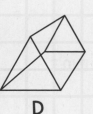

D

E

F

G

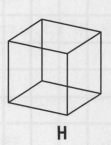

H

	A	B	C	D	E	F	G	H
Prism	✔							
Pyramid								

Measuring length

Learning objective: to convert units of length and measure lines accurately

We measure length using kilometres, metres, centimetres and millimetres.

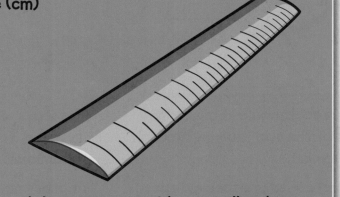

10 millimetres (mm) = 1 centimetre (cm)

100 centimetres = 1 metre (m)

1000 metres = 1 kilometre (km)

2.8cm = 2cm 8mm = 28mm

3.45m = 3m 45cm = 345cm

6.5km = 6km 500m = 6500m

To measure the length of lines accurately you may need to use millimetres.

A Complete these.

1. 58 mm = _____ cm

2. 10.67 m = _____ cm

3. 910 cm = _____ m

4. 13.5 cm = _____ mm

5. 8.3 km = _____ m

6. 94 mm = _____ cm

7. 3700 m = _____ km

8. 14.6 cm = _____ mm

Your work on decimals on page 6 will help you with these conversions.

DEFINITION

cm: Means centimetre.
m: Means metre.
km: Means kilometre.

B

Use a ruler to measure the length of each line accurately in millimetres.

1. _____

2. _____

3. _____

4. _____

5. _____

6. _____

C

The perimeter of a shape is the distance all around the edge.
These shapes are all regular, so each side is the same length.

Measure the length of one side of each shape in millimetres. Use this measurement to work out the perimeter of each shape.

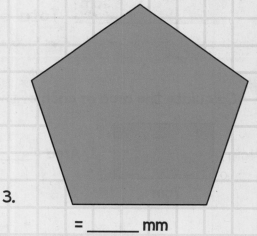

1. = _____ mm

2. = _____ mm

3. = _____ mm

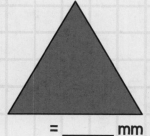

4. = _____ mm

Use millimetres when you need to measure something accurately.

51

Area

The area of a shape is the amount of surface that it covers.

The area of a rectangle or square can be calculated by multiplying the length by the width.

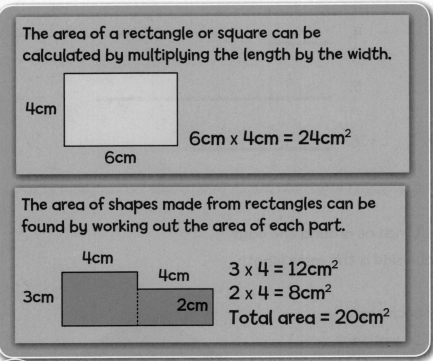

4cm

6cm

$6cm \times 4cm = 24cm^2$

The area of shapes made from rectangles can be found by working out the area of each part.

4cm

4cm

3cm

2cm

$3 \times 4 = 12cm^2$
$2 \times 4 = 8cm^2$
Total area $= 20cm^2$

Area is measured in square units, such as square centimetres (cm^2) and square metres (m^2).

A

Calculate the area of each of these.

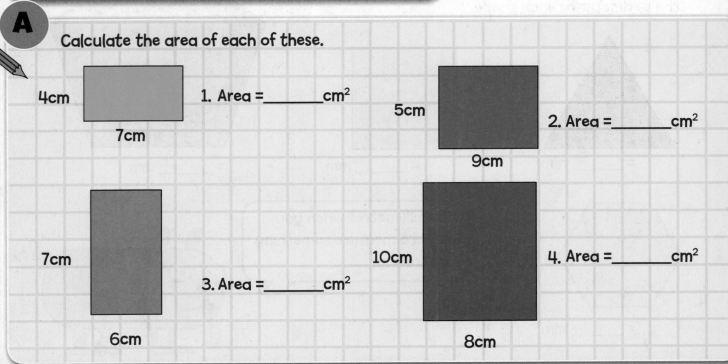

4cm

7cm

1. Area = _____ cm^2

5cm

9cm

2. Area = _____ cm^2

7cm

6cm

3. Area = _____ cm^2

10cm

8cm

4. Area = _____ cm^2

B

Write the area for each of these shapes.

6cm

3cm

1. Area =_____cm²

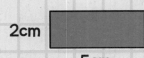

2cm

5cm

2. Area =_____cm²

4cm

4cm

3. Area =_____cm²

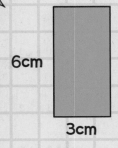

5cm

3cm

4. Area =_____cm²

C

Calculate the area of these shapes. Work out the area of each rectangle within the shape first.

8cm

2cm 2cm

4cm

1.   Area =_____cm²

5cm

3cm

2cm

2cm

2. Area =_____cm²

9cm

4cm

3cm

6cm

3. Area =_____cm²

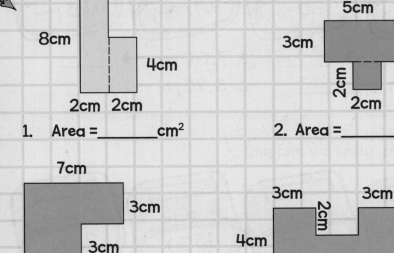

7cm

3cm

3cm

4cm

4. Area =_____cm²

3cm   3cm

2cm

4cm

9cm

5. Area =_____cm²

8cm

2cm

4cm   4cm

4cm   2cm

2cm

6. Area =_____cm²

53

24-hour clock

Timetables and digital watches often use the 24-hour clock.

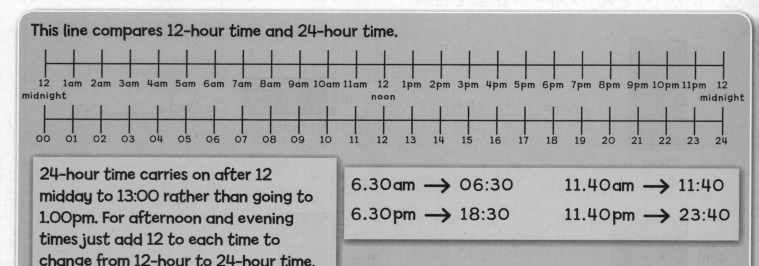

This line compares 12-hour time and 24-hour time.

24-hour time carries on after 12 midday to 13:00 rather than going to 1.00pm. For afternoon and evening times just add 12 to each time to change from 12-hour to 24-hour time.

6.30am → 06:30   11.40am → 11:40
6.30pm → 18:30   11.40pm → 23:40

A   Write these times as 24-hour clock times.

1. 10.25am → __:__   2. 9.55am → __:__   3. 7.00pm → __:__
4. 4.30pm → __:__   5. 9.47am → __:__   6. 5.25pm → __:__

B   Write these times as 12-hour clock times, using am and pm.

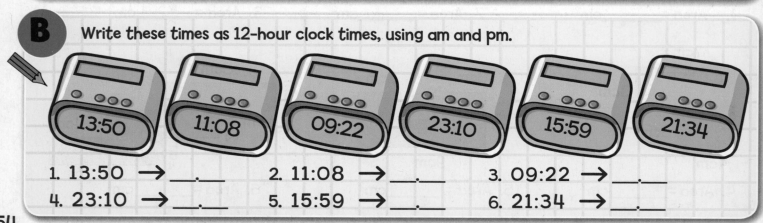

1. 13:50 → __.__   2. 11:08 → __.__   3. 09:22 → __.__
4. 23:10 → __.__   5. 15:59 → __.__   6. 21:34 → __.__

C

Write these same times in two lists, showing the times as both 24-hour and 12-hour times.

07:00

11.35am

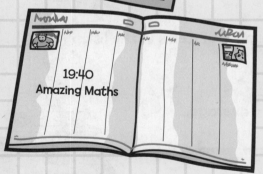

19:40
Amazing Maths

Event	12-hour time	24-hour time
Alarm wake up	7.00am	07:00

taxi
7.15pm

14:18

Meet for coffee
10.00am

D

6th July, 1989 at 11.45pm was a very special time.

It could be written as:

23:45 6.7.89!

Write the time in 24-hour clock to find out what was special about 8.10pm on 20th October 2010.

_____

Work out some other special dates and times.

Find out about the date and time when you were born!

Data

Learning objective: to solve problems using the mode, median and mean

Averages are middle scores or the most common numbers.
There are three main types of average: mean, mode and median.

Look at this example to compare the three types of average.
This chart shows the goals scored by the players in a football team.
Does Sam score above the average number of goals for the team?

Player	Sam	Brent	Jason	Ali	Carl
Goals scored	8	4	8	6	9

> When working out the median and there is an even amount of numbers, you take the two middle numbers, add them together and divide by two.

Mode is the most common number.
2 players scored 8 goals so that is the mode.

Median is the middle number when listed in order – 4, 6, 8, 8, 9.
8 is the median number of goals.

For the mean add the numbers and divide the total by the number of items in the list.
4 + 6 + 8 + 8 + 9 = 35   35 ÷ 5 = 7
So the mean average is 7 goals.

Sam is an above-average goal scorer compared with the mean average, and at the average for the mode and median.

A

A packet of fruit-drops is divided into piles of different flavours.

grape (purple) = 3	lemon (yellow) = 4	strawberry (pink) = 7
orange (orange) = 4	lime (green) = 8	raspberry (red) = 4

1. Which is the most common amount of sweets of the same flavour? _____
   Is this the mean, mode or median? _____

2. If the piles of sweets were put in order of size, which size pile would be in the middle?
   _____
   Is this the mean, mode or median? _____

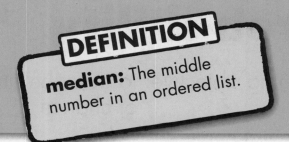

DEFINITION

median: The middle number in an ordered list.

B

These are the heights of a group of five children.

Ben: 140cm	Sam: 130cm	Eve: 140cm	Amy: 150cm	Jon: 190cm

1. What is the mode height?
2. What is the median height?
3. What is the mean height?
4. How many children are above the mean average height?
5. Which child is at the mean average height?
6. Another child joins the group. Her height is 120cm. What is the mean average height for the group now?

Remember!
Mode is the most common number.

C

These are the hand-spans for a group of 10 children.

A hand-span is measured from the tip of the little finger to the tip of the thumb.

10cm	8cm	12cm	9cm	8cm	10cm	13cm	11cm	9cm	10cm

1. Median: _____   2. Mode: _____   3. Mean: _____

Challenge

Read this graph and find the median, mode and mean averages of the number of hours of TV watched each day in one week.

4. Median: _____   5. Mode: _____   6. Mean: _____

Probability

Learning objective: to describe and predict outcomes using the language of chance

We can use a probability scale to show how likely an event is to happen.

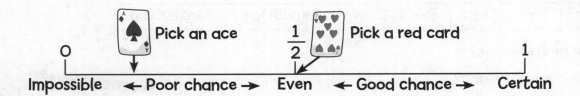

Pick an ace

$\frac{1}{2}$ Pick a red card

0   1

Impossible   ← Poor chance →   Even   ← Good chance →   Certain

Method 1

Even chance, or evens, is an equal chance of something happening as not happening. We also say a 1 in 2 chance, 1/2 chance or a 50:50 chance.

Example: In a pack of playing cards there is an even chance of picking a red card.

Method 2

Dice experiments are useful for testing probabilities.

On a normal die, the probability of throwing a 2 is 1 in 6 or 1/6. That is because there is only one number 2 on the die out of a possible six numbers.

0 means something will never happen. 1 means something will definitely happen.

A These ten playing cards are shuffled and placed face down. Choose from the statements at the bottom to show the probability of turning over these cards.

1. a multiple of 2
2. a diamond
3. a multiple of 5

4. a number greater than 4
5. the queen of diamonds
6. the 9 of diamonds

Impossible   Poor chance   Evens   Good chance   Certain

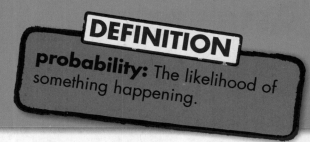

B Using a die, write the chance of throwing each of these.

Choose one of the following probabilities ➔   1 in 2   1 in 3   1 in 6

1. a six _____

2. an even number _____

3. a multiple of 3 _____

4. a number greater than 4 _____

5. a number less than 4 _____

6. a one _____

C Colour the correct number of beads in this bag to match these probabilities.

- There is a 50:50 chance of picking out a red bead from the bag.
- There is a 1 in 6 chance of picking out a blue bead from the bag.
- There is a 1/4 chance of picking out a green bead from the bag.
- It is impossible to pick out a yellow bead from the bag.
- There is a 1 in 12 chance of picking out a black bead from the bag.

How many of each colour are there?

1. _____ red beads

2. _____ green beads

3. _____ blue beads

4. _____ black beads

5. _____ yellow beads

Answers

Pages 6-7 Decimals

A
1. 0.2
2. 0.35
3. 0.71
4. 0.96
5. 8.18
6. 8.4
7. 8.53
8. 8.79
9. 8.95
10. 16.18
11. 16.4
12. 16.53
13. 16.79
14. 16.99

B
Leatherback turtle   462.9kg
Green sea turtle   355.3kg
Loggerhead turtle   257.8kg
Flatback turtle   78.15kg
Hawksbill turtle   62.65kg
Kemp's Ridley turtle 60.45kg

C 2. 3.58, 3.85, 5.38, 5.83, 8.35, 8.53

Pages 8-9 Place value

A
1. 13.5
2. 96.7
3. 6.85
4. 33.46

B
1. 35 litres
2. 98.5km
3. 25kg

C

×10 →		
8.2	82	820
0.82	8.2	82
0.082	0.82	8.2

(÷10)

×10 →		
0.6	6	60
0.06	0.6	6
0.006	0.06	0.6

(÷10)

Pages 10-11 Mental calculation

A
1. 6   2. 16   3. 7   4. 18
5. 9   6. 12   7. 5   8. 6
9. 7   10. 63   11. 9   12. 6

B
1. 20   2. 5   3. 16   4. 11
5. 12   6. 5   7. 2   8. 47

C
1. 19 − (12 - 5) = 12
2. 16 − (10 - 6) = 12
3. 22 − (5 + 5) = 12
4. (6 + 13) − 7 = 12
   or 6 + (13 - 7) = 12
5. (24 - 6) − 6 = 12
6. 20 − (10 - 2) = 12

D
1. 48   2. 7   3. 8
4. 21   5. 9   6. 20

Pages 12-13 Square numbers

A and B

	0	1	2	3	4	5	6	7	8	9	10
0	0	0	0	0	0	0	0	0	0	0	0
1	0	1	2	3	4	5	6	7	8	9	10
2	0	2	4	6	8	10	12	14	16	18	20
3	0	3	6	9	12	15	18	21	24	27	30
4	0	4	8	12	16	20	24	28	32	36	40
5	0	5	10	15	20	25	30	35	40	45	50
6	0	6	12	18	24	30	36	42	48	54	60
7	0	7	14	21	28	35	42	49	56	63	70
8	0	8	16	24	32	40	48	56	64	72	80
9	0	9	18	27	36	45	54	63	72	81	90
10	0	10	20	30	40	50	60	70	80	90	100

C
1. 24, 48
2. 15, 12
3. 46
4. 18, 77
5. 6, 50
6. 39, 92

D
1. 16
2. 49
3. 36
4. 81
5. 1
6. 4
7. 100
8. 9
9. 64
10. 25

Pages 14-15 Multiples and factors

A
1. (1, 8) (2, 4)
2. (1, 20) (2, 10) (4, 5)
3. (1, 24) (2, 12) (3, 8) (4, 6)
4. (1, 28) (2, 14) (4, 7)

B
1. 4, 8, 12, 16, 20, 24, 28, 32, 36, 40
2. 3, 6, 9, 12, 15, 18, 21, 24, 27, 30
3. 6, 12, 18, 24, 30, 36, 42, 48, 54, 60
4. 5, 10, 15, 20, 25, 30, 35, 40, 45, 50
5. 10, 20, 30, 40, 50, 60, 70, 80, 90, 100
6. 8, 16, 24, 32, 40, 48, 56, 64, 72, 80

C
1. 15, 30   2. 12, 24
3. 20, 40   4. 24, 48
5. 30, 60   6. 12, 24, 36

D

Factor of 24 / Multiple of 3 Venn diagram:
10, 2, 4, 1, 16 (Factor of 24 only)
12, 3, 24, 6 (intersection)
15, 20, 9, 30, 18, 25 (Multiple of 3 only)

Pages 16-17 Prime numbers

A
1. The number 5 cannot be divided by 2 or 3 or 4. So the number 5 is prime.
2. The number 6 can be divided by 2 or 3. So the number 6 is not prime.
3. The number 7 cannot be divided by 2 or 3 or 4 or 5 or 6. So the number 7 is prime.
4. The number 3 cannot be divided by 2. So the number 3 is prime.
5. The number 8 can be divided by 2 or 4. So the number 8 is not prime.
6. The number 11 cannot be divided by 2 or 3 or 4 or 5 or 6 or 7 or 8 or 9 or 10. So the number 11 is prime.

B The hidden primes are: 7, 11, 13, 17, 19, 23, 29

C They can't be divided whatever you do
The smallest prime is number two
Then come three and five and seven
The next prime is of course eleven
Thirteen is next upon the scene
Seventeen follows, and then nineteen.

Pages 18-19 Written addition

A
1. 9468
2. 7803
3. 4479

B
1. 9625   4. 7869
2. 9803   5. 7077
3. 6078   6. 6435

C
1. 3420km   4. 4849km
2. 5803km   5. 4490km
3. 6281km

D

```
    4   6  [3]  8
+   9  [1]  6  [3]
  [1] [3]  8  0 [1]
```

Pages 20-21 Written subtraction

A 1. 3146   2. 5668
   3. 4370

B 1. 3847 - 1762 = 2085
   2. 7943 - 2486 = 5457
   3. 4115 - 2936 = 1179

C 1. 1161m
   2. 1381m
   3. 1279m
   4. Caribbean and Bering
   5. Caribbean
   6. Indian and Atlantic

Pages 22-23 Written multiplication

A 1. 1444   2. 3108
   3. 456   4. 3286

B 1. 720 hours   3. 700g
   2. 928km   4. 735

C

Items	Amount in 1 pack	Number of packs	Total number of items
Pencils	28	76	2128
Chalk	15	33	495
Sharpeners	26	19	494
Erasers	48	14	672
Pens	52	58	3016
Crayons	34	47	1598

D 1. 543 x 6 = 3258
   2. 456 x 3 = 1368
   3. 456 x 3 = 1368

Pages 24-25 Written division

A 1. 162 r2   3. 47 r1
   2. 73 r2   4. 231 r2

B 1 ⟶ 271 ÷ 6
   2 ⟶ 608 ÷ 3
   3 ⟶ 315 ÷ 8
   4 ⟶ 454 ÷ 5
   5 ⟶ 149 ÷ 6
   6 ⟶ 398 ÷ 7
   7 ⟶ 259 ÷ 9
   8 ⟶ 458 ÷ 9
   9 ⟶ 359 ÷ 10

C

Day of the week	Eggs collected	Number of Full boxes (6 eggs)	Eggs left over
Monday	627	104	3
Tuesday	572	95	2
Wednesday	700	116	4
Thursday	644	107	2
Friday	683	113	5
Saturday	594	99	0
Sunday	735	122	3

Pages 26-27 Rounding numbers

A Liverpool – 469000
   Bradford – 293700
   Sheffield – 439900
   Derby – 229400
   Birmingham – 970900
   Nottingham – 249600
   Bristol – 420600
   Plymouth – 243800

B 1. 800   4. 1200
   2. 500   5. 5900
   3. 100   6. 13700

C 1. 16kg   2. 21kg
   3. 34kg   4. 45kg

D 1. 0.93   2. 7.08
   3. 12.95   4. 7.59
   5. 2.91   6. 30.08

Pages 28-29 Decimal calculations

A 1. 67.83   3. 91.81
   2. 84.76   4. 85.51

B 1. 43.02   3. 37.76
   2. 47.23   4. 41.78

C 1. 26.63 l   3. 68.01kg
   2. 63.91m   4. 81.23m

D 1. 0.76   4. 0.09
   2. 0.51   5. 1.34
   3. Eileen and Nikki

Pages 30-31 Simplifying fractions

A 1. $6 \div 3 = 2$ $21 \div 3 = 7$
   So $\frac{6}{21}$ is the same as $\frac{2}{7}$.
   2. $9 \div 3 = 3$ $15 \div 3 = 5$
   So $\frac{9}{15}$ is the same as $\frac{3}{5}$.
   3. $4 \div 2 = 2$ $6 \div 2 = 3$
   So $\frac{4}{6}$ is the same as $\frac{2}{3}$.
   4. $12 \div 6 = 2$ $18 \div 6 = 3$
   So $\frac{12}{18}$ is the same as $\frac{2}{3}$.

B 1. $15 \div 5 = 3$ $40 \div 5 = 8$
   So $\frac{15}{40}$ is the same as $\frac{3}{8}$.
   2. $14 \div 2 = 7$ $16 \div 2 = 8$
   So $\frac{14}{16}$ is the same as $\frac{7}{8}$.
   3. $8 \div 2 = 4$ $12 \div 2 = 6$
   So $\frac{8}{12}$ is the same as $\frac{4}{6}$
   4. $20 \div 10 = 2$ $30 \div 10 = 3$
   So $\frac{20}{30}$ is the same as $\frac{2}{3}$

Other possible answers:
$20 \div 5 = 4$ $30 \div 5 = 6$
So $\frac{20}{30}$ is the same as $\frac{4}{6}$
$20 \div 2 = 10$ $30 \div 2 = 15$
So $\frac{20}{30}$ is the same as $\frac{10}{15}$

C $\frac{9}{18}$ and $\frac{1}{2}$.
   $\frac{10}{15}$ and $\frac{2}{3}$.
   $\frac{18}{24}$ and $\frac{3}{4}$.
   $\frac{7}{28}$ and $\frac{1}{4}$.
   $\frac{12}{15}$ and $\frac{4}{5}$.
   $\frac{50}{60}$ and $\frac{5}{6}$.
   $\frac{11}{33}$ and $\frac{1}{3}$

Pages 32-33 Comparing fractions

A

1. $\frac{1}{3} = \frac{2}{6} = \frac{3}{9} = \frac{4}{12} = \frac{5}{15} = \frac{6}{18}$

2. $\frac{1}{4} = \frac{2}{8} = \frac{3}{12} = \frac{4}{16} = \frac{5}{20} = \frac{6}{24}$

3. $\frac{1}{2} = \frac{2}{4} = \frac{3}{6} = \frac{4}{8} = \frac{5}{10} = \frac{6}{12}$

4. $\frac{2}{3} = \frac{4}{6} = \frac{6}{9} = \frac{8}{12} = \frac{10}{15} = \frac{12}{18}$

B 1. >
   2. <
   3. <
   4. >

C

Number line: 0   0.1   0.2   0.25   0.3   0.4   0.5   0.6   0.7   0.75   0.8   0.9   1

$0.1 \rightarrow \frac{1}{10}$ $0.2 \rightarrow \frac{1}{5}$

$0.25 \rightarrow \frac{1}{4}$ $0.3 \rightarrow \frac{3}{10}$

$0.4 \rightarrow \frac{2}{5}$ $0.5 \rightarrow \frac{1}{2}$

$0.6 \rightarrow \frac{6}{10}$ and $0.6 \rightarrow \frac{3}{5}$

$0.7 \rightarrow \frac{7}{10}$ $0.75 \rightarrow \frac{3}{4}$

$0.8 \rightarrow \frac{4}{5}$ $0.9 \rightarrow \frac{9}{10}$

Answers

Page 33 cont.

D 1. $\frac{1}{4}$, $\frac{3}{8}$, $\frac{1}{2}$, $\frac{10}{16}$

2. $\frac{1}{6}$, $\frac{1}{3}$, $\frac{6}{12}$, $\frac{3}{4}$

Pages 34-35 Equivalents

A 1. 30%   5. 80%
2. 20%   6. 10%
3. 7%   7. 65%
4. 22%   8. 12%

B 1. 0.5   4. ⅖
2. 25%   5. 0.34
3. 5%   6. 70%

C 1. ¼, 25%   4. ³⁄₁₀, 30%
2. ⁴⁄₈, 50%   5. ²⁄₅, 40%
3. ⁷⁄₁₀, 70%   6. ⁴⁄₈, 50%

D 1. 1%   3. 80%
2. 80%   4. 80%

Pages 36-37 Percentages

A 1. $\frac{2}{5}$ 2. $\frac{4}{5}$ 3. $\frac{1}{4}$

B 1. 70%   4. 84%
2. 90%   5. 76%
3. 80%

C 1. 7cm   5. 35ml
2. 27km   6. 20m
3. 4 litres   7. 60g
4. 12kg   8. 200mm

D

	50%	25%	10%	40%	5%
60m	30m	15m	6m	24m	3m
50m	25m	12.5m	5m	20m	2.5m
300m	150m	75m	30m	120m	15m
250m	125m	62.5m	25m	100m	12.5m

Pages 38-39 Proportion

A
1. $\frac{1}{3}$ 2. $\frac{1}{4}$

3. $\frac{1}{2}$ 4. $\frac{2}{3}$

5. $\frac{2}{5}$ 6. $\frac{3}{4}$

B 1.

Pineapples	Oranges	Total
1	4	5
2	8	10
5	20	25
8	32	40
10	40	50

2.

Bananas	Peaches	Total
2	3	5
4	6	10
12	18	30
16	24	40
20	30	50

C 1. butter 150g   flour 200g
   carrots 100g   sugar 60g
   eggs 50g   walnuts 40g
2. flour 180g   butter 90g
   sugar 60g   choc chips 30g

D butter 300g   flour 400g
   carrots 200g   sugar 120g
   eggs 100g   walnuts 80g

Pages 40-41 2D shapes

A 1. triangle   4. hexagon
2. quadrilateral   5. heptagon
3. pentagon   6. octagon

B 1. rectangle   2. parallelogram
3. trapezium   4. square
5. kite   6. rhombus

C 1. always   4. always
2. never   5. sometimes
3. always   6. always

Pages 42-43 Angles

A

Straight angle	4.
Acute	1.
Obtuse	2.
Right angle	3.

B

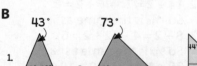

C

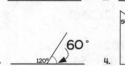

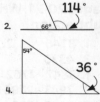
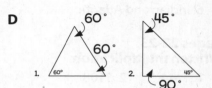

D

Pages 44-45 Moving shapes

A 1. rotated   2. reflected
3. translated   4. reflected
5. translated   6. rotated

Pages 46-47 Coordinates

A 1. (3, 5)   2. (8, 8)

B 1. Triangle B
   (4, 1) (6, 4) (7, 1)
2. Triangle C
   (0, 3) (3, 2) (3, 6)
   Triangle D
   (5, 2) (5, 6) (8, 3)
3. Triangle E
   (0, 5) (4, 5) (4, 8)
   Triangle F
   (4, 2) (4, 5) (8, 5)

Pages 48-49 3D shapes

A 1. A triangular prism has
   2 triangular faces and 3
   rectangular faces.
2. A cube has 6 square faces.
3. A tetrahedron has 4 triangular
   faces.
4. A hexagonal prism has
   2 hexagonal faces and 6
   rectangular faces.
5. A square-based pyramid has

1 square face and 4 triangular
faces.
6. A cuboid has 4 rectangular
faces and 2 square faces.

B

	A	B	C	D	E	F	G	H
Prism	✔	✔	✔	✔	✔			✔
Pyramid						✔	✔	

Pages 50-51 Measuring length

A 1. 5.8cm 2. 1067cm
   3. 9.1m 4. 135mm
   5. 8300m 6. 9.4cm
   7. 3.7km 8. 146mm
B 1. 35mm 2. 52mm 3. 26mm
   4. 18mm 5. 63mm 6. 37mm
C 1. 108mm 2. 112mm
   3. 175mm 4. 96mm

Pages 52-53 Area

A 1. 28cm^2 3. 42cm^2
   2. 45cm^2 4. 80cm^2
B 1. 18cm^2 3. 16cm^2
   2. 10cm^2 4. 15cm^2
C 1. 24cm^2 4. 33cm^2
   2. 19cm^2 5. 30cm^2
   3. 54cm^2 6. 48cm^2

Pages 54-55 24-hour clock

A 1. 10:25 2. 09:55
   3. 19:00 4. 16:30
   5. 09:47 6. 17:25
B 1. 1.50pm 2. 11.08am
   3. 9.22am 4. 11.10pm
   5. 3.59pm 6. 9.34pm
C Alarm wake up
   7.00am   07:00
   Meet for coffee
   10.00am   10:00
   Dentist
   11.35am   11:35
   Bus time
   2.18pm   14:18
   Taxi
   7.15pm   19:15

Amazing Maths
   7.40pm   19:40
D 20:10 20.10.2010

Pages 56-57 Data

A 1. 4/mode
   2. 4/median
B 1. 140cm 4. 1
   2. 140cm 5. Amy
   3. 150cm 6. 145cm
C 1. Median 10cm
   2. Mode 10cm
   3. Mean 10cm
   Challenge
   4. Median 2 hours
   5. Mode 2 hours
   6. Mean 3 hours

Pages 58-59 Probability

A 1. There is an even chance
   of picking a multiple of 2.
   2. There is a certain chance
   of picking a diamond.
   3. There is a poor chance
   of picking a multiple of 5.
   4. There is a good chance of
   picking a number over 4.
   5. It is impossible to pick the
   queen of diamonds.
   6. There is a poor chance of
   picking the 9 of diamonds.
B 1. 1 in 6 2. 1 in 2
   3. 1 in 3 4. 1 in 3
   5. 1 in 2 6. 1 in 6
C 1. 12 red 2. 6 green
   3. 4 blue 4. 2 black
   5. 0 yellow

Index